THE JOURNEY

THE WICKED WOOD

PART ONE of THE JOURNEY

Written by
Hilary Jane Jones

Design and Photography by
Tracey Swain

BRIAR RIDGE BOOKS

First published in 2012 by Briar Ridge Books
Whittingslow, Church Stretton, Shropshire SY6 6PZ

Printed and bound in the UK by

Gomer Press, Llandysul, Ceredigion

ISBN Print: 978-0-9572371-0-0

This book is available to download in pdf format and will be available as an eBook. Please see website for details.
www.briarridgebooks.co.uk

1 3 5 7 9 10 8 6 4 2

Cover image Clunton Coppice, Shropshire

Live life with love and laughter

seeing all layers of the living

landscapes around you

This book is dedicated to
all those with an inner child
who still believe in fantasy
and faerie tales

Welcome to Part One of The Journey

Enter the darkness and tread
the inner depths of The Wicked Wood.
Here fantasy fires the imagination,
dread and fear fill each footstep.

Look very closely:
what you think you see may surprise you.
Reality or a trick of the eye? You decide?

I set out at the break of day

My destination, far away,

Beside the path an old man stood,

"Beware" he warned, "the wicked wood".

He pointed 'cross the misty dale:

Who knew what lay beneath its veil?

Here and there, from out the shroud,

A tree-top broke the sea of cloud.

The land lay still, no creature stirred,

I listened; not a sound was heard.

I turned - the old man gone was he!

Where once he stood a thorny tree...

...Needles of frost were all I saw,

The old man he was there no more.

Shivering now, I turned away,

Walked fast into the brightening day.

The hours flew past, the wood drew near,

The old man's words rang in my ears:

Despite the fear that filled his voice

My destiny allowed no choice.

No other path could take me there,

Towards my destination where

The Mountains of Eternity

Rose skywards from a mystic sea...

...Where faeries danced and tumbling streams

Flowed through a land infused with dreams.

But first I knew I had to tread

The twisted path whose course I'd dread.

Tress, gnarled and knotted, filled that place,

Holly and bramble scratched my face,

Roots snaked through unrelenting ground:

Darkness and danger lurked all round.

"Come, quick!" I'm sure I heard him say,

"I'm down amongst the roots - this way":

Cautious, I knelt, surprised to see

A tiny creature 'neath the tree...

...And yet the old man looked the same,

Knew my journey, knew my name:

Pointing, he climbed into my hand,

"Far down that track, your promised land".

He bade me place him in a tree

Its dying limbs reached out to me:

"This wood is cursed, you're cursed as well,

But you can help defeat the spell...

...You must, before the break of day,

Cross through the wood and make your way

Past dens where nymphs and spirits hide,

To freedom on the other side."

Down the spiralling stems he slid,

Amongst the tangled roots he hid,

Far out of sight the man had flown,

Left me to cross the wood alone.

Desperate to escape the place

I turned - felt something brush my face:

The wood all round me came alive,

As right before my very eyes...

...A snake tree squirmed in tangled glee,

Twisted, contorted, laughed at me,

Shivered, as through its tangled frame

An evil wind hissed out my name.

Its branches danced in frenzied whirls,

Lambs tails adorned Medusa's curls.

I fled before the serpent's spell

Drew me into its arms as well.

Then suddenly from darkened skies

Came devil-birds with piercing cries,

Wide, claw-tipped wings, outstretched in flight,

Forked tails, dark eyes - as black as night.

"Begone!" the old man roared, "Away!

This one is mine... seek other prey."

He turned towards the searing sun:

I looked up - all the birds were gone.

Arms raised, he chanted, conjured clouds:

Soft snowflakes fell, concealed the ground.

I watched as scarlet blood-drops formed

Along a hedge of icy thorns,

Each drop, a life lost in the wood

...ten thousand edged the path I trod.

"Go now," he said, "for in this cold

The snakes and demons have no hold...

...They cannot catch you while it lasts,

But once it's gone they'll follow fast".

I slipped and slid along the path:

I swear I heard the old man laugh.

His laughter echoed through the trees,

Amplified on frigid breeze,

From north and south, from east and west,

Above, below: no break, no rest.

I raised cold hands to shield my ears,

Stumbled on: sharp, frozen tears

Spilled from my eyes. I screamed "No more!"

Fell to my knees: the snowy floor...

...Began to melt, the laughter died,

The only sound, now, dripping ice.

Again the old man came in sight,

Leading the way towards the light.

Before me ran a peaceful brook,

A fallen tree-bridge: "Look, oh look!

See how the darkness melts away,

Across the stream, a bright new day.

Go quickly now, but don't look back,

Fast fall their feet upon the track,

They must not catch you, demons all,

They'll try to trick you, make you fall...

...And if they reach you, as they might,

They'll drag you to their world of night,

Eternal darkness, evil spells:

That side lies Heaven - this side, Hell!"

I crossed the bridge, sharp claws reached out,

The air filled with the old man's shouts:

"Vile creatures, you shall burn and die,

You'll never have this child of mine."

His fingers snapped, flames flashed, trees burned,

Sky filled with fire – the creatures turned:

Nowhere to run, nowhere to hide,

Spine-chilling screams rose up... then died.

I turned, forsook their world of night,

Before my eyes a wonderous sight:

Fragrant bluebells, trees fresh green,

The prettiest place I'd ever seen.

The old man stopped, stood by the brook,

Tears filled his eyes, his old hands shook,

"Go now", he said, "my spirit child,

Escape the wood, run free, run wild...

...Fate will not let me leave this place,

But I have seen my sweet child's face:

Your destiny lies far from mine,

Though I will love you for all time."

My hand reached back: "Come, father, please",

He'd gone, all I could see were trees.

Rain fell like tears, then way up high

A rainbow kissed the weeping sky.

END OF PART ONE

WHERE OUR JOURNEY BEGAN

The Journey was born from love and respect for the beauty of nature and the countryside in and around Shropshire and the Welsh borders. Where magic and mystery so often linger unseen, Hilary and Tracey have woven a fantasy that will captivate your heart and mind, and leave you wanting to know where *The Journey* is going next, and where is it's ultimate destination...

Haunting images with hidden secrets.

Reality, or a trick of the eye? You decide?

The Journey Continues

in Part Two

The Faerie Glen

The wicked wood at last was gone,

Through dew kissed flowers I journeyed on.

I'm sure I heard the old man say,

"Fae folk now will guide your way".

THE
FAERIE GLEN

PART TWO of THE JOURNEY

Hilary Jane Jones   ◆   Tracey Swain

POETESS AND PAINTER OF LIGHT

Hilary Jane Jones is a writer and poet,
born and bred in Shropshire.

Tracey Swain is a photographer who fell in love with
the landscape and light of Shropshire on a short visit
and promptly moved there in 2007.

A love of fantasy and a mutual respect for each
other's work brought them together to create books
that celebrate the landscapes that surround them and
at the same time challenge the reader to look a little
deeper to see the magic that hides within each scene.

IMAGE CREDITS

Nearly all images in this book are taken by landscape
photographer Tracey Swain in her home county of
Shropshire and chosen from her archives by Tracey
and Hilary to complement each verse.

All the images are pure with the exception of two,
those on pages 35 and 67 which
we felt needed some digital magic.
Anything else you believe you see is real.

The images on pages 39 and 49 were taken
by Hilary herself as she created
The Journey on her walks with her dogs.

For further information about the works of

Hilary Jane Jones and Tracey Swain

including how to purchase images from

The Journey please go to

www.briarridgebooks.co.uk